How to use this book

Follow the advice, in italics, given for you on each page.
Support the children as they read the text that is shaded in cream.
Praise *the children at every step!*
Detailed guidance is provided in the Read Write Inc. Phonics Handbook.

9 reading activities
Children:
1 *Practise reading the speed sounds.*
2 *Read the green, red and challenge words for the non-fiction text.*
3 *Listen as you read the introduction.*
4 *Discuss the vocabulary check with you.*
5 *Read the non-fiction text.*
6 *Re-read the non-fiction text and discuss the 'questions to talk about'.*
7 *Re-read the non-fiction text with fluency and expression.*
8 *Answer the questions to 'read and answer'.*
9 *Practise reading the speed words.*

Speed sounds

Consonants *Say the pure sounds (do not add 'uh').*

f ff	l ll	m mm	n nn kn	r rr	s ss se	v ve	z zz s	**sh**	th	ng nk

b bb	c k **ck**	d dd	g gg	h	j g **ge**	p **pp**	qu	t tt	w wh	x	y	ch tch

Vowels *Say the vowel sound and then the word, eg 'a', 'at'.*

at	hen head	in	on	up	day	see happy	high	blow

zoo	look	car	for door snore	fair	whirl	shout	boy

*Each box contains one sound but sometimes more than one grapheme. Focus graphemes are **circled**.*

Green words

| c<u>ar</u> | M<u>ar</u>k | f<u>ar</u> | p<u>ar</u>k | j<u>ar</u> | l<u>ar</u> <u>ge</u> |
| <u>sh</u>op | lo<u>ng</u> | wi<u>th</u> | list | aw<u>ay</u> | box |

<u>sh</u>opp` ing ⟶ <u>sh</u>opp ing    coff` ee ⟶ coff ee

mu<u>sh</u>` r<u>oo</u>ms ⟶ mu<u>sh</u>r<u>oo</u>ms    <u>sh</u>am` p<u>oo</u> ⟶ <u>sh</u>amp<u>oo</u>

pa<u>ck</u>` et ⟶ pa<u>ck</u>et

p<u>ar</u>k ⟶ p<u>ar</u>ked   n<u>ee</u>d ⟶ n<u>ee</u>ded

<u>th</u>i<u>ng</u> ⟶ <u>th</u>i<u>ng</u>s   egg ⟶ eggs

plum ⟶ plums   t<u>ar</u>t ⟶ t<u>ar</u>ts

Red words

of the I we to
was she some

Jam tarts

Introduction

Do you like going shopping? A girl and her brother go to the supermarket with their mum. Mum needs lots of things, but the children would like a treat!

Written by Gill Munton

Vocabulary check

Discuss the meaning (as used in the non-fiction text) after the children have read the word.

	definition
needed	*had to get*
plums	*soft, juicy fruit*
mushrooms	*little umbrella-shaped things that you eat*

Punctuation to note:

Mum Mark	*Capital letters for names*
We It She	*Capital letters that start sentences*
.	*Full stop at the end of each sentence*
!	*Exclamation mark to show surprise*
...	*'Wait and see' dots*

Mum needed lots of things from the shop.

I got in the car with Mum and Mark.

We went to the shop. It was not far away. Mum parked in the car park.

Mum had a long list.

Shopping list

coffee

pop

eggs

cheese

plums

nuts

mushrooms

shampoo

Mum got a big jar of coffee and six cans of pop.

She got a box of large eggs and a packet of cheese.

She got a box of plums and a packet of nuts.

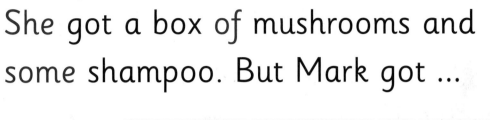

She got a box of mushrooms and some shampoo. But Mark got ...

6 Real fruit jam tarts

... six jam tarts!

Questions to talk about

Re-read the page. Read the question to the children. Tell them whether it is a FIND IT *question or* PROVE IT *question.*

FIND IT	**PROVE IT**
✓ *Turn to the page*	✓ *Turn to the page*
✓ *Read the question*	✓ *Read the question*
✓ *Find the answer*	✓ *Find your evidence*
	✓ *Explain why*

Page 9:	FIND IT	*Why did they go to the shop?*
Page 10:	FIND IT	*Where did Mum park the car?*
Page 11:	FIND IT	*What was at the top of Mum's shopping list?*
Page 12:	FIND IT	*What did Mum get in a big jar?*
Page 13:	FIND IT	*What sort of eggs did Mum get?*
Page 14:	PROVE IT	*What sort of fruit did Mum get?*
Page 15:	FIND IT	*What did Mum get last?*
Page 16:	PROVE IT	*Do you think Mum was cross with Mark? Why/Why not?*

Questions to read and answer ⭐ ✷

(Children complete without your help.)

1 Mum got a big jar of **pop** / **coffee** / **nuts**.

2 Mum got **three** / **six** / **ten** cans of pop.

3 Mum got a box of **cheese** / **shampoo** / **mushrooms**.

4 Mark got **jam tarts** / **nuts** / **plums**.

5 Mark got **six** / **ten** / **three** jam tarts.